Writing Performance Counts

Evaluate Your Writing

... and Prepare for Writing Assessment

Acknowledgments
Product Development: Kent Publishing Services, Inc.
Design and Production: Signature Design Group, Inc.
Illustrations: 4, 5, 7, 11 and 12, Richard Kolding; 25, 26, Charles Shaw
Photos: 41, Kit Kittle/Corbis; 49, 59, Richard Hamilton Smith/Corbis; 61, Warren Morgan/Corbis; 62, Fotografia, Inc./Corbis; 76, Bettmann/Corbis; 77 top, Randy Faris/Corbis; 77 bottom, Araldo de Luca/Corbis

ISBN: 1-56936-790-6
Options Publishing, Inc.
P.O. Box 1749
Merrimack, NH 03054-1749
TOLL FREE: 800-782-7300 • FAX: 866-424-4056
www.optionspublishing.com

Table of Contents

Think and Read

➤ **Myths are stories that people invent to explain things they don't understand about nature. Think about something that has puzzled you. Write down what you remember about the experience.**

_____

_____

_____

The Birth of Spring

Ceres (SERE-rees) was the ancient Roman goddess of all growing things. She made the entire earth more fruitful and taught people the art of farming plants for food. Because Ceres blessed her followers' harvests, Roman farmers made offerings of grain and vegetables to her.

Ceres' chief joy was her daughter Proserpina (PRO-ser-PEEH-nah). One beautiful day, Proserpina was walking in the fields of Sicily. She bent to pluck a perfect daffodil from the field. With a rumble, the ground suddenly opened beneath her feet. A chariot drawn by huge black horses thundered out of the earth. Pluto, god of the Underworld, held the reins. He lifted Proserpina in his large arms and carried her below the earth to be his queen.

When she learned of her daughter's fate, Ceres was filled with sorrow. Nothing on Earth could flourish without her care. Crops did not grow and the grass withered. The olive vines and apple trees bore no fruit. The king of the gods, Jupiter, saw how the Earth was suffering and summoned Ceres. Ceres begged Jupiter to force Pluto to return her daughter. Jupiter agreed, but there was one condition. Anyone who ate anything in the Underworld was doomed to remain there. If Proserpina had eaten anything, she would have to stay forever.

Unknowingly, Proserpina had eaten three pomegranate seeds. Jupiter did not want to anger Pluto by taking away his queen. However, Jupiter knew that the people and animals on Earth would starve if Ceres could not see her daughter. He offered a compromise. Each year, Proserpina would remain in the Underworld one month for each seed she had eaten. For the other nine months she could live with her mother.

Since that day, no plants could live for the three months Proserpina was in the Underworld with Pluto. But when Proserpina returned to her mother, buds and blossoms sprang forth from the trees. Farmers plowed their fields, sowed their seeds, and looked forward to harvesting their crops. The world rejoiced with Ceres at the return of her daughter and the birth of spring, summer, and fall.

➤ **Liam's class read the myth of Ceres and Proserpina. Each student was assigned to write a letter from Proserpina in the Underworld to her mother on Earth. Liam made a topic web to organize his ideas about what Proserpina would say. Use the web to answer questions 1-3.**

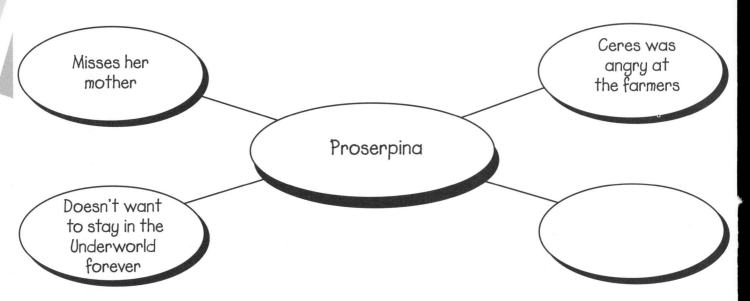

1. **Which idea could Liam use for the blank circle?**

    Ⓐ Pluto wants to send her back   Ⓒ Eats olive seeds

    Ⓑ Misses her friends   Ⓓ Plants live for three months

2. **Which idea is not correct in Liam's topic web?**

    Ⓐ Misses her mother

    Ⓑ Doesn't want to stay in the Underworld

    Ⓒ Ceres was angry at the farmers

    Ⓓ All of Liam's ideas are correct.

3. **Write down two more ideas Liam could use for his topic web.**

    _____

    _____

➤ **Liam knew that some Roman myths were also told in Ancient Greece. He wanted to find the Greek names for the characters in the myth of Ceres and Proserpina. Use the glossary below to answer questions 4-6.**

GLOSSARY OF GREEK MYTHOLOGICAL CHARACTERS

Aphrodite—goddess of love and beauty
Athena—goddess of wisdom
Demeter—goddess of the harvest
Hera—goddess of hearth and home
Hermes—god of speed and messages
Mars—god of the Underworld
Persephone—goddess of the seasons
Zeus—god of all gods and ruler of Mount Olympus

Noodle Around

During prewriting, check that your ideas relate to your main idea. Which questions will help Liam check the link between his ideas and the main idea? Discuss it with a friend.

4. **What is the Greek name for Ceres?**

   Ⓐ Athena   Ⓒ Demeter

   Ⓑ Aphrodite   Ⓓ Hera

5. **What is the Greek name for Jupiter?**

   Ⓐ Mars   Ⓒ Hermes

   Ⓑ Zeus   Ⓓ Athena

6. **Which book would help Liam find an explanation about the myth of Ceres?**

   Ⓐ *The Children's Book of Myths*

   Ⓑ *The Story of Ceres and Proserpina*

   Ⓒ *The Story of Zeus and Hera*

   Ⓓ *Ceres and Proserpina: A Myth Explained*

Lesson 2: Prewriting and Referencing

➤ **Now check your answers. If you answered a question incorrectly, study the correct answer.**

1. **Which idea could Liam use for the blank circle?**

   Answer Ⓑ is the correct answer. Proserpina would certainly miss her friends, especially the Roman farmers.

2. **Which idea is not correct in Liam's topic web?**

   Answer Ⓒ is the correct answer. The story tells us that Ceres taught people the art of farming and blessed her followers' harvest.

3. **Write down two more ideas Liam could use for his word web.**

   Answers could include topics related to the story. For example:

   The Earth was suffering because she was gone: She misses the fields of flowers: Ceres asked Jupiter to let Proserpina go.

4. **What is the Greek name for Ceres?**

   Answer Ⓒ is the correct answer; *Demeter* and *Ceres* are the Greek and Roman names for the goddess of the harvest.

5. **What is the Greek name for Jupiter?**

   Answer Ⓑ is the correct answer; *Zeus* is the Greek name for *Jupiter*.

6. **Which book would help Liam find an explanation about the myth of Ceres?**

   Answer Ⓓ is correct. The first three books will simply tell stories.

➤ **Here is a chance to work on your prewriting and referencing skills. Answer the questions on the next three pages.**

1. One of the best places to look for new words is called a *thesaurus*. A thesaurus is a reference book that lists groups of words with the same meanings. The words on the left are taken from *The Birth of Spring*. Draw a line from each word in the left column to the group of words in the right column that means the same thing.

   a. reins   **1.** buds, develops, grows, opens, flourishes

   b. blossoms   **2.** destiny, end, chance, fortune, circumstance

   c. condition   **3.** dull, shriveled, faded, deteriorated, pale

   d. withered   **4.** circumstance, plight, predicament, situation

   e. fate   **5.** bridle, check, bit, control, curb

2. One method of prewriting is called *freewriting*. Set your timer for five minutes. Using your memory and experiences, write as much as you can about something that frightened or puzzled you when you were young.

_____

_____

_____

_____

_____

_____

_____

3. Next, make a brief outline of a letter to your best friend describing your ideas about what frightened or puzzled you.

_____

_____

_____

_____

_____

4. Another way to organize ideas is a topic web. From the outline you wrote above, choose the main idea for a word web. Write it in the middle of the web below.

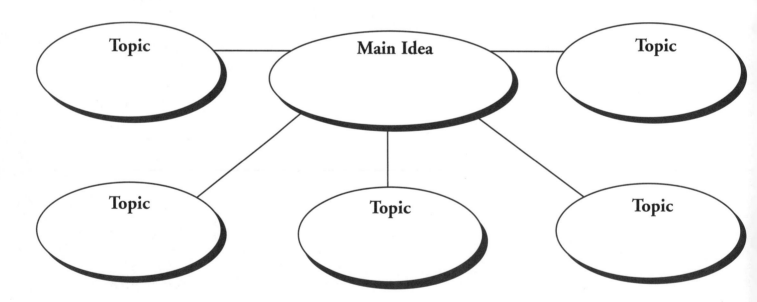

5. With your main theme in mind, choose four or five topics that connect to that idea. Write them in your web.

6. Choose one of the topics from your web. Write some ideas that would support or add to the topic.

_____

_____

7. Take these ideas, and look at them next to your main idea. Do all of these terms relate to that main idea in some way? Explain how they do or do not relate to the main idea.

_____

_____

_____

8. Choose one of the words in the four topic circles in your web. Look it up in a thesaurus. Write down all the variations you find.

_____

_____

9. Look up the dictionary meanings for two of the alternate words you found in the thesaurus. Use each of them in a sentence about your topic or theme.

_____

_____

_____

Lesson 2: Prewriting and Referencing

➤ **Read the first part of Liam's rough draft of his letter. Then answer questions 1–6.**

Dear Mother Ceres,

   (1) I am so lonely here in the dark Underworld. (2) When the seasons change, the weather does, too. (3) I miss my friends and our picnics in the countryside. (4) When we used to gather flowers. (5) Pluto has been kind to me. (6) He gave me a delicious pomegranate today. (7) This afternoon I ate some pomegranate seeds.

   (8) I was hungry but I only ate three of them. (9) I only had those few seeds because after I ate those three Pluto told me something that made me sad he said that that if you eat something here you have to stay here forever as my queen I don't want to stay here. (10) Pluto told me that since I ate pomegranate seeds I have to stay here but I don't want to.

1. **What kind of sentence is sentence 4?**

   Ⓐ complete   Ⓒ run-on

   Ⓑ predicate   Ⓓ incomplete

2. **Which two sentences are repetitive or redundant?**

   Ⓐ sentences 6 and 7   Ⓒ sentences 3 and 4

   Ⓑ sentences 9 and 10   Ⓓ sentences 1 and 2

3. How could Liam combine sentences 5, 6, and 7 to make two stronger sentences? Write the new sentences below.

_____

_____

_____

_____

4. What kind of sentence is sentence 9? Explain why this sentence contains errors.

Ⓐ complicated   Ⓒ run-on

Ⓑ predicate   Ⓓ incomplete

_____

_____

5. Write a topic sentence that explains the main idea of this draft.

_____

_____

6. Which of the following sentences does not belong in this draft?

Ⓐ sentence 2   Ⓒ sentence 5

Ⓑ sentence 9   Ⓓ sentence 4

Lesson 3: Composing and Revising

➤ **Now check your answers. If you answered a question incorrectly, study the correct answer.**

1. **What kind of sentence is sentence 4?**

   Answer Ⓓ is correct. This sentence is missing information. It needs an introductory clause with a noun and a verb. For example:
   I miss those days when we used to gather flowers.

2. **Which two sentences are repetitive or redundant?**

   Answer Ⓑ is correct. These two sentences repeat one idea, although each sentence is constructed differently.

3. **How could Liam combine sentences 5, 6, and 7 to make two stronger sentences? Write the new sentences below.**

   Answers will vary. An example might be:
   This afternoon, Pluto was very kind and gave me a delicious pomegranate. I ate some of the seeds.

4. **What kind of sentence is sentence 9? Explain why this sentence contains errors.**

   Answer Ⓒ is correct. Sentence 9 runs on without enough punctuation or breaks between ideas.

5. **Write a topic sentence that explains the main idea of this draft.**

   Answers will vary, but your sentence should include the main idea that Proserpina is homesick and lonely.

6. **Which of the following sentences does not belong in this draft?**

   Answer Ⓐ is correct. Although the story of Ceres and Proserpina is a myth about the seasons, Liam's letter is not.

➤ **Here is a chance to work on your composing and revising skills. Answer the questions on the next three pages.**

1. **Write a brief paragraph that puts the following events in order.**

   a. Proserpina eats the seeds

   b. Proserpina returns to Earth

   c. Proserpina goes to the Underworld

   d. Ceres appeals to Jupiter

   _____

   _____

   _____

   _____

   _____

   _____

Writer's Tip

Adjectives and adverbs are like salt and pepper: they help spice up your writing. But remember, too much of either one doesn't "taste" very good. Choose your descriptive words carefully when you're writing a story.

2. **Repeating ideas in your writing can make your reader lose interest. Indicate the sentences and phrases that are repetitive in the following paragraph by drawing a line through each one.**

   Many Greek and Roman myths feature the same stories and characters. Many of the stories and characters are alike. Their names are very different, however. Names like Demeter and Ceres, Aphrodite and Venus, and Mars and Pluto refer to the same gods and goddesses. Although the names are different, the stories featuring these characters helped ancient people understand the world around them.

Lesson 3: Composing and Revising

3. **There are different kinds of sentence errors.**
   - **A sentence fragment is a sentence that is missing information.**
   - **A comma splice is two or more complete sentences separated only by a comma.**
   - **A run-on sentence has too much information and no punctuation.**

Identify each kind of error in the following sentences.

a. That she only ate three seeds. _____

b. Pluto handed her a pomegranate before she could eat more he told her she

would have stay in the Underworld. _____

c. She only ate three seeds from the fruit, she thought she would

eat more. _____

4. **One of the easiest ways to vary your writing is to combine sentences using conjunctions such as *but, and, for, with,* or *until.* Combine the following groups of sentences using conjunctions. Rewrite each new sentence below.**

a. The Sun made a bet with the Wind. They made a bet that one of them could

make a man take off his coat. _____

_____

b. The Wind blew cold air on the man. The man clutched his coat more

tightly around himself. _____

_____

c. Laughing, the Sun shone brightly. The Sun made it warmer. As it grew

warmer, the man took off his coat. _____

_____

5. **Read the following story draft. Which sentence does not belong in the story? Explain why.**

(1) The queen issued a decree throughout the land that any girl who could shoot an arrow through the golden apple would become the queen's successor. (2) Many girls came with their bows and arrows, but none of them could shoot far enough or straight enough to hit the apple. (3) Hundreds failed, and the queen feared she would never find a worthy candidate. (4) The queen had hundreds of gems and thousands of gold coins.

(5) Living in the back of the village there was a girl named Eleanor. (6) The queen became desperate to find a young woman who could take over her duties and inherit her castle. (7) Since her toddler days, Eleanor had been practicing archery. (8) If anyone could hit the golden apple, she could.

_____

_____

6. **What would be the best place for sentence 5? Does it need extra information? Explain your answer.**

_____

_____

7. **This story needs a conclusion to sum up the main idea. Write two sentences to conclude the story draft.**

_____

_____

_____

➤ **Read the end of Liam's draft. This section has groups of underlined words. Editing questions will be asked about them.**

(11) Pluto said that I was doomed to remain in the Underworld.
(12) Oh! I cried for a very, very long time. (13) I really <u>will have wanted</u> to see you, Mother Ceres, back in our home. (14) Would you, please beg "Jupiter" to see if he will let me return to Earth? (15) If I come home soon, I will be so happy. (16) We can pick <u>flower's, and, have</u> picnics.

(17) Their aren't any flowers or trees growing here at all. (18) The Underworld is not the best place for plants, animals, or human beings. (19) That is because it's <u>two hot</u> for living things down here. (20) It is <u>very</u> difficult to get used to staying here and acting as Pluto's queen. (21) I don't like living in the Underworld at all. (22) Please write back to me soon because I miss you and everything on Earth.

Love, Proserpina

1. **What part of speech is *Oh!* in sentence 12?**

   Ⓐ adjective   Ⓒ preposition

   Ⓑ adverb   Ⓓ interjection

2. **Choose a replacement for the verb phrase in sentence 13.**

   Ⓐ will want   Ⓒ want

   Ⓑ had wanted   Ⓓ no change needed

3. Correct the punctuation errors in sentence 14. Rewrite the sentence.

_____

_____

4. Which is the correct punctuation for sentence 16?

   Ⓐ We can pick flower's, and, have picnics.

   Ⓑ We can pick flower's and have picnics.

   Ⓒ We can pick flowers, and have picnic's.

   Ⓓ We can pick flowers and have picnics.

Writer's Tip

Make sure the adverb you choose to describe a verb is strong and tells exactly what you mean. Is something the **best**, or is it really just **good**?

5. The correct word in sentence 19 is *too*. What are words like *too* and *two* called?

   Ⓐ synonyms   Ⓒ antonyms

   Ⓑ homonyms   Ⓓ pseudonyms

6. What part of speech is the word *very* in sentence 20? How could you rewrite this sentence to help Liam make it better?

   Ⓐ adjective   Ⓒ preposition

   Ⓑ adverb   Ⓓ interjection

_____

_____

_____

_____

Noodle Around

Verb phrases are two verbs linked together to present an action. Which question asks about verb phrases? Discuss it with a friend.

➤ **Now check your answers. If you answered a question incorrectly, study the correct answer.**

1. **What part of speech is *Oh!* in sentence 12?**

   Answer Ⓓ is correct. *Oh!* is an interjection, an exclamation made in the middle of a declarative sentence.

2. **Choose a replacement for the verb phrase in sentence 13.**

   Answer Ⓒ is correct. Proserpina actively wishes to see her mother now. I really want to see you, Mother Ceres, back in our home.

3. **Correct the punctuation errors in sentence 14.**

   The quotation marks around Jupiter are unnecessary and so is the comma after *would you*. The corrected sentence reads as follows:

   Would you please beg Jupiter to see if he will let me return to Earth?

4. **Which is the correct punctuation for sentence 16?**

   Answer Ⓓ is correct. *Flowers* is the correct plural form, and no comma is necessary.

5. **The correct word in sentence 19 is *too*. What are words like *too* and *two* called?**

   Answer Ⓑ is correct. Homonyms are words that sound similar but have different meanings.

6. **What part of speech is the word *very* in sentence 20? How could you rewrite this sentence to help Liam make it better?**

   Answer Ⓑ is correct. *Very* is an adverb, a descriptive word that modifies a verb. The corrected sentence might read as follows:

   It is very difficult to stay here as Pluto's queen.

Try It

➤ **Here is a chance to work on your editing skills. Answer the questions on the next three pages.**

1. **The following sentences need quotation marks. Add quotation marks by using these editing symbols ⌄⌄ ⌄⌄. Add the other punctuation marks needed to make these sentences correct.**

    a. If I can't leave soon said Proserpina I will be very hungry even hungrier than I am now?

    b. You must remain in the Underworld said Pluto as my wife and my queen!

    c. Please let my daughter return to Earth said Ceres?

2. **Apostrophes show where letters have been dropped in a contraction. Write the following words as contractions.**

    a. you are _____   **d.** they are _____

    b. does not _____   **e.** should not _____

    c. cannot _____   **f.** here is _____

3. **Homonyms are words that sound alike but have different meanings. Circle each correct word to complete the sentences below.**

    a. I'm going to the seashore no matter what the (whether / weather) is like.

    b. When I'm there, I'm going to look for a (pair / pear) of conch shells.

    c. If I stand (stationary / stationery), maybe I'll hear the ocean in one of them.

    d. The sound might be (two / too) (weak / week) to (here / hear).

©2001 Options Publishing, Inc.

Lesson 4: Editing

4. Superlatives are adjectives that make comparisons to the greatest degree. Follow the example and write the superlative form of the following adjectives.

Example: big, biggest

a. large _____

d. shiny _____

b. fine _____

e. blue _____

c. bad _____

f. good _____

5. Many writers have trouble deciding when to use an apostrophe and when not to use an apostrophe with words that end in *s*. Insert apostrophes where they are needed in the following paragraph. Use this editing mark $\lor$.

Cape Cod has many of our countrys most beautiful seashores. The Seagull Beachs shoreline is full of rocks and seashells. My brothers hobby is to collect seashells, especially if the seashells shapes are interesting.

6. Choosing the correct verb tense can be difficult, especially if you are trying to talk about different times in the same piece of writing. Circle the underlined verbs that are in the wrong tense.

Last summer we <u>went</u> to a beach I really like, <u>call</u> Children's Beach. This beach was on the island of Nantucket. We <u>spend</u> lots of time there. The Beach <u>will look</u> out at Nantucket Harbor, and it <u>has</u> a snack bar and a playground. Maybe this summer we <u>will have visited</u> Children's Beach again.

7. **An adverb modifies a verb, but sometimes writers choose an adjective when they are supposed to use an adverb. Circle the correct modifier for each sentence below.**

   a. I don't feel (good / well).

   b. She can run really (quick / quickly).

   c. My teacher says we should read books (carefully / careful).

   d. We (slowly / slow) walked down the trail in the woods.

8. **Interjections are used to create a sense of feeling in a narrative. For each interjection, write a short sentence using that word.**

   a. Oh! _____

   b. Help! _____

   c. But! _____

   d. Rats! _____

9. **There are exactly ten mistakes in the following paragraph. Edit the paragraph using the editing symbols found on page 112.**

   When I was little storm's scared me. Why they happen. My mother told me that people in the skie were bowling. She said that every lightning bolt will be a "strike." I believe her until I turned ate. I found a pear of books at the library that described storms really good.

➤ **Now you are going to read and evaluate a story that Keiko wrote. It is about a greedy queen. Her writing needs your help. Before you begin, read the checklist below.**

Writing Checklist

Keiko will earn her best score if she achieves the following:

Ideas	• Ideas are original • Topic is clearly identified • Ideas support the topic
Organization	• Ideas are related and presented in correct order • Strong beginning, middle, and end
Creativity and Word Choice	• Words used appropriately • Creative descriptions • Words enhance ideas
Sentence Structure	• Complete sentences • Clearly written and easy to understand
Spelling and Punctuation	• Few or no errors

➤ **These are the directions that Keiko was given.**

Directions: In the story of King Midas, the greedy monarch asks for the power to turn everything he touches into gold. Write a story about a king or queen who is greedy. Use your imagination. Think of a strong beginning, middle, and end.

(1) A long long time ago lived a ruler named Queen Ursula who was always discontented. (2) Queen Ursula aksed a great spirit to give her special powers. (3) He said that it would be very difficult. (4) When Queen Ursula woke up the next day, she desided to try her new power. (5) She walked from room to room and touched all of her belongings. (6) Before her eyes, each thing turned to gelatin as she touched it. (7) Even just a tap and it becomes transparent.

(8) Soon everything, even her miniature poodle was made of gelatin. (9) Queen Ursula rushed quickly outside and touched her garden, her car, and her boat. (10) The beautiful shimmering colors inlcuded purple and rose. (11) Purple is made by mixing blue and red together. (12) You can make other colors by mixing parts of red and yellow and blue. (13) Everyone admired the new gelatin palace and it's beautiful colors.

(14) People from all over came to see the towers sway back and forth in the breeze and the castle moat filled with real gelatin fish! (15) They photographed the fantastic castle and the famous queen who thought she was happy.

(16) But soon the queen was getting tired of all the gelatin. (17) The bright colors hurt her eyes and the jigling made her nervous. (18) When she tried to get something to eat, it all tasted ecsactly the same! (19) When she tried to take a nap, her bed wiggled and jiggled. (20) She finally called the spirit back to the palace. (21) "Please take this power away from me," she asked. (22) The spirit laughed and said "I told you so." (23) The spirit told her to promise she would be happy with things if he changed them back. (24) Queen Ursula promised.

(25) When she woke up all of her things were just as they had been before she made her fateful wish. (26) Her poodle barked her birds sang and her doorbell rang instead of making a squishy sound. (27) Queen Ursula rolled over on her nice firm bed and called for brekfast. (28) The cook had just come back from vacashun. (29) She didnt know about the Queen's wish. (30) She sent up fresh made orange juice and a big crystal bowl of gelatin in all the colors of the rainbow!

©2001 Options Publishing, Inc.

➤ **Now answer the questions about Keiko's story.**

1. How would you edit the incorrect usage in sentence 7?

   _____

   _____

2. Which word could be added to give a stronger description about the poodle in sentence 8?

   Ⓐ fluffy   Ⓒ slimy

   Ⓑ prickly   Ⓓ gooey

3. The first paragraph is missing a sentence. Where?

   Ⓐ between sentences 5 and 6   Ⓒ between sentences 4 and 5

   Ⓑ between sentences 1 and 2   Ⓓ between sentences 3 and 4

4. Which sentences do not belong in this story?

   Ⓐ sentences 10 and 11

   Ⓑ sentences 1 and 2

   Ⓒ sentences 29 and 30

   Ⓓ sentences 11 and 12

Writer's Tip

When developing a series of events in a story, keep in mind that one event might affect a later event.

5. Rewrite sentence 13 so it is correct.

   _____

   _____

   _____

6. **Find the misspelled words in the story. Write them below, and give their correct spellings.**

_____

_____

7. **Each of the following sentences uses an adjective instead of an adverb. Rewrite each sentence correctly.**

   a. She sent up fresh made orange juice and a big crystal bowl of gelatin in all the colors of the rainbow!

   _____

   _____

   b. The bright colors hurt her eyes and the jiggly made her nervous.

   _____

   _____

   c. Her fluffy poodle barked ferocious at the queen.

   _____

   _____

8. **Rewrite sentence 26 so that it is punctuated correctly.**

_____

_____

9. You were already asked about the missing sentence in paragraph 1. That sentence would have given some important information. Rewrite paragraph 1 for Keiko so that the missing details are provided.

_____

_____

_____

_____

_____

_____

10. Keiko's assignment was to write about a greedy monarch. In her story, the greedy queen has a change of heart. Imagine if Queen Ursula decided not to give back her new power. Write a new ending to the story.

_____

_____

_____

_____

_____

_____

_____

Evaluate Keiko's Writing

➤ **Here is a guide for evaluating writing. It is called a rubric. Rubrics are used to grade tests. Use this rubric to evaluate Keiko's story.**

Writing Rubric

Score	Ideas	Organization	Creativity and Word Choice	Sentence Structure	Spelling and Punctuation
4	• Ideas are original • Topic is clearly identified • Ideas support the topic	• Ideas are related and presented in correct order • Strong beginning, middle, and end	• Words used appropriately • Creative descriptions • Words enhance ideas	• Complete sentences • Clearly written and easy to understand	• Few or no errors
3	• Some ideas are original • Most ideas support the topic	• Most ideas are related and presented in correct order • Good beginning, middle, and end	• Most words used appropriately • Some creative descriptions • Words support ideas	• Many sentences are complete • Most sentences are clearly written and easy to understand	• Some errors
2	• Few ideas are original • Ideas wander from topic • Some details support the topic	• Some ideas are related and presented in correct order • Weak beginning, middle, and end	• Some words used appropriately • Few creative descriptions	• Some run-on or fragmented sentences • Some sentences are unclear	• Many errors
1	• Ideas are incomplete • Few details support the topic	• Few ideas are related and presented in correct order • No real beginning, middle, and end	• Few words used appropriately • No attempt at creative descriptions	• Several run-on or fragmented sentences • Many sentences are unclear	• Serious errors
0	• No attempt	• No attempt	• No attempt	• No attempt	• No attempt

➤ Give Keiko's writing a score of 0 to 4 for each category. Explain why you gave her that score.

Ideas _____

score

_____

_____

Organization _____

score

_____

_____

Creativity and Word Choice _____

score

_____

_____

Sentence Structure _____

score

_____

_____

Spelling and Punctuation _____

score

_____

©2001 Options Publishing, Inc.

➤ **Read the directions below. Then, read the checklist that you and your teacher will use to evaluate your writing.**

Directions: Now it is your turn to write your own myth. Explain how night and day came to be. Think about your characters. Decide what kinds of reasons you will invent to explain your myth. Remember to organize your ideas and write clearly. Use details to help your reader imagine the situation.

Writing Checklist

I will earn my best score if I achieve the following:

Ideas	• Ideas are original • Topic is clearly identified • Ideas support the topic
Organization	• Ideas are related and presented in correct order • Strong beginning, middle, and end
Creativity and Word Choice	• Words used appropriately • Creative descriptions • Words enhance ideas
Sentence Structure	• Complete sentences • Clearly written and easy to understand
Spelling and Punctuation	• Few or no errors

Plan Your Writing

➤ **Use these pages to plan your writing. You might find this graphic organizer helpful.**

The Beginning
(Characters and Setting)

The Middle
(The Problem and Events)

The End
(The Solution or Final Outcome)

_____

_____

_____

_____

_____

_____

_____

_____

Lesson 6: Your Turn to Write

Plan Your Writing

Writer's Tip

Before writing, make a list of details to describe how your characters look, feel, and act. Using descriptive words adds color to your writing.

_____

_____

_____

_____

_____

_____

_____

_____

_____

_____

_____

_____

_____

_____

Writer's Tip

Many people like fictional stories, but no one likes fictional spelling. Check your spelling carefully.

Writer's Tip

Use a variety of sentence types in your writing. Use a mixture of short and complex sentences to keep the reader interested.

Lesson 6: Your Turn to Write

Write Your Final Draft

▶ **Use all the skills you have learned in this unit to score well on a final draft. Remember to carefully proofread your work before you give it to your teacher.**

1 _____

2 _____

3 _____

4 _____

5 _____

6 _____

7 _____

8 _____

9 _____

10 _____

11 _____

12 _____

13 _____

14 _____

15 _____

16 _____

17 _____

18 _____

19 _____

20 _____

21 _____

22 _____

23 _____

24 _____

25 _____

26 _____

27 _____

28 _____

29 _____

30 _____

31 _____

32 _____

33 _____

► **Here is the same rubric you used to evaluate Keiko's story. Now use it to evaluate your own myth.**

Writing Rubric

Score	Ideas	Organization	Creativity and Word Choice	Sentence Structure	Spelling and Punctuation
4	• Ideas are original • Topic is clearly identified • Ideas support the topic	• Ideas are related and presented in correct order • Strong beginning, middle, and end	• Words used appropriately • Creative descriptions • Words enhance ideas	• Complete sentences • Clearly written and easy to understand	• Few or no errors
3	• Some ideas are original • Most ideas support the topic	• Most ideas are related and presented in correct order • Good beginning, middle, and end	• Most words used appropriately • Some creative descriptions • Words support ideas	• Many sentences are complete • Most sentences are clearly written and easy to understand	• Some errors
2	• Few ideas are original • Ideas wander from topic • Some details support the topic	• Some ideas are related and presented in correct order • Weak beginning, middle, and end	• Some words used appropriately • Few creative descriptions	• Some run-on or fragmented sentences • Some sentences are unclear	• Many errors
1	• Ideas are incomplete • Few details support the topic	• Few ideas are related and presented in correct order • No real beginning, middle, and end	• Few words used appropriately • No attempt at creative descriptions	• Several run-on or fragmented sentences • Many sentences are unclear	• Serious errors
0	• No attempt	• No attempt	• No attempt	• No attempt	• No attempt

➤ **Give your own writing a score of 0 to 4 for each category. Explain why you gave yourself that score.**

score

Ideas _____

_____

_____

score

Organization _____

_____

_____

score

Creativity and Word Choice _____

_____

_____

score

Sentence Structure _____

_____

_____

score

Spelling and Punctuation _____

_____

Lesson 1

➤ **Do you have a favorite place to visit? You might go to a swimming pool every day, or a friend's backyard, or a basketball court to shoot hoops. On the lines below, explain why you continue to go back to this place. Then read the article that follows.**

_____

_____

Patches of Green

Parks are very important to cities. They add important elements to city life such as relaxation, exercise, and community time. We need more city parks so that people can enjoy these good things.

Busy residents can relax in city parks. Parks surround us with plants and flowers, not metal, glass, and concrete. In a park a city resident can stare at a

Golden Gate Park, San Francisco

bed of daffodils instead of at a bank of computers. Some parks are close to offices and schools so that it is easy for us to get there. For example, in New York City, Bryant Park is right behind the library. People visit the park to soak up the sun.

Parks also give people in cities a chance to exercise. San Francisco's Golden Gate Park has several miles of leafy trails for strolling and running. Boston Commons has ice skating on its pond in winter.

Some parks have tennis courts or fitness trails. People who live in apartments and work inside tall buildings might not be able to stay healthy and exercise without parks.

Another important reason we need city parks is that people can gather to socialize. City families are often separated during the day. Parents and other caregivers go to work. Children go to school. Older people are sometimes in their apartments for most of the day. In a city park, everyone in a family or group of friends can meet. Parks help people to keep family and community ties.

Boston Commons, Boston, Massachusetts

Bryant Park, New York City

Relaxation, exercise, and community are just some of the reasons that city parks are so important. The next time you think of a city and its concrete, metal, and glass, remember that somewhere in the middle there should be a patch of green. That patch is a park, where people can take breaks, take walks, and take time to be with their families. Without parks, city residents will not be as happy or as healthy as they can be. We need to preserve our patches of green, our parks. The more parks we build in our urban communities, the more all city residents will benefit.

➤ **Shira's class was assigned to write a persuasive essay. Shira decided to write an editorial for the local paper about why her school needs a skating park. She started by writing a list of pros and cons for building a skating park. Use Shira's list below to answer questions 1–3.**

Pro	Con
a. Great exercise	a. Dangerous activity
b. Gets kids together	b. Noise bothers the community
c. Really cool looking	c. Unattractive
	d. I don't like to in-line skate

1. Write one more pro and one more con for Shira's list.

   _____

   _____

2. **Which person probably would think the park is bothersome?**

   Ⓐ one of Shira's classmates   Ⓒ someone whose office faces the park

   Ⓑ Shira's baby brother   Ⓓ the people building the park

3. **Why should Shira consider not using the last item under *Con?***

   Ⓐ It doesn't make sense.   Ⓒ It should be in the pro column.

   Ⓑ It is too short.   Ⓓ It only gives an opinion.

➤ **Shira's teacher asked the class to use the computer to search the Internet for sites about their topics. Look at the Web addresses Shira found. Use her list to answer questions 4–6.**

Search for (skating parks) go

MATCHING SITES FOUND (page 1 of 546)

1. **www.marcysblades.com**
   Buy the perfect pair for a promenade in the park!
2. **www.radwheels.com**
   Learn bladers' secrets, techniques, and favorite parks in Bass River.
3. **www.brschools.edu**
   Notes from the May 29, 2000, meeting of the Bass River School Board, with proposal for skating park.
4. **www.brpr.org**
   Regulations and rules for city parks.
5. **www.bassriver.net/chron.htm**
   Today's news, editorials, sports, comics, and more.

4. **Which Web site would not be useful to Shira?**

   Ⓐ www.marcysblades.com   Ⓒ www.radwheels.com

   Ⓑ www.bassriver.net/chron.htm   Ⓓ www.brschools.edu

5. **Which Web site will give Shira the most information about the pros and cons of setting up a skating park?**

   Ⓐ www.brschools.edu

   Ⓑ www.radwheels.com

   Ⓒ www.bassriver.net/chron.htm

   Ⓓ www.brpr.org

Writers develop a list of pros and cons to research both sides of an issue. Which questions ask you to evaluate the pros and cons? Discuss it with a friend.

6. **If Shira would like to try a new search, write two keywords that might be helpful.**

➤ **Now check your answers. If you answered a question incorrectly, study the correct answer.**

1. **Write one more pro and one more con for Shira's list.**

    Answers may include pros such as these: new benefit for school, keeps kids near school instead of wandering about city streets; **and cons such as:** possible injuries, so many kids gathering together may get into trouble.

2. **Which person probably would think the park is bothersome?**

    Answer Ⓒ is correct. Someone whose office faces a skating park might find the noise and traffic unappealing.

3. **Why should Shira consider not using the last item under *Con*?**

    Answer Ⓓ is correct; a pro or con that involves only the writer's opinion will not seem very strong to readers.

4. **Which Web site would not be useful to Shira?**

    Answer Ⓐ is correct; a site that sells something will probably not help her understand the issue of the school's skating park.

5. **Which Web site will give Shira the most information about the pros and cons of setting up a skating park?**

    Answer Ⓐ is correct because the minutes of the school board meeting will present arguments from both sides of the debate.

6. **If Shira would like to try a new search, write two keywords that might be helpful.**

    Answers might include school, extreme sports, skating.

Try It

➤ **Here is a chance to work on your prewriting and referencing skills. Answer the questions on the next three pages.**

1. Writing pros and cons for the first time is easiest if you are involved in the debate or argument. Imagine your parents have told you in-line skating is too dangerous for you to learn. Write a list of pros (your point of view) and cons (their objections) in the chart below.

Pro	Con

2. Sometimes the most effective way to begin writing a persuasive essay is to try brainstorming—thinking of all the things you know about a particular subject. On the lines below, brainstorm all the things you know about the parks in your area. What are they used for? Who goes to parks in your area?

_____

_____

_____

_____

_____

Lesson 2: Prewriting and Referencing

3. The more specific your keywords, the better the information you will find on the Internet. Take one specific item from your brainstorming list in question 2. Using a computer in your classroom or library, enter the keywords in a search to find a Web site about parks in your area. Write a brief paragraph about what you found in the search.

_____

_____

_____

_____

4. There are different kinds of Web sites for different kinds of organizations. Do you know the Web abbreviations for *education, government, commerce,* and *organization?* Draw a line to match the four below with their names.

a. www.virginia.edu   1. Virginia State Legislature

b. www.virginia.gov   2. The Virginia Shop

c. www.virginia.com   3. The University of Virginia

d. www.virginia.org   4. Virginia Foundation for the Humanities

5. Where else could Shira look for information about skating parks? Write a list of 3 resources for her.

_____

_____

_____

6. **At the beginning of this unit, you wrote about why you return to your favorite place again and again. Complete this chart listing four reasons why you should return to your favorite place and four reasons why you shouldn't return to you favorite place.**

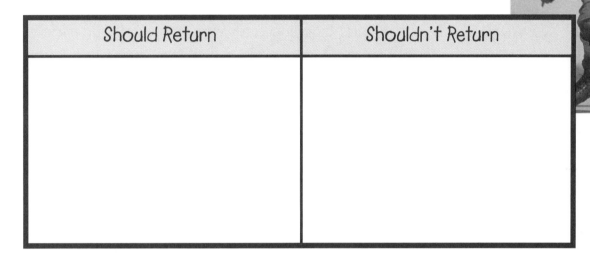

Should Return	Shouldn't Return

7. **Here is a list of different arguments about going to school year-round. Sort the list into pros and cons. Add them to the chart below.**

- Keeps children out of trouble
- Keeps families from taking vacations
- Keeps children from forgetting what they've learned
- Lowers the chance for students to earn money from summer jobs
- Lowers the number of students held back

Pro	Con

Lesson 2: Prewriting and Referencing

➤ **Read this part of Shira's rough draft. Then answer questions 1–6.**

To the Editor:

(1) Mayor LeRoux is wrong. (2) Our school should get the in-line skating park we want. (3) She says that building a skating park at our middle school isn't necessary. (4) I believe that our school (5) A skating park could be built near the fieldhouse. (6) Building the park near the fieldhouse would make it easy for skaters to change into their skates and to store their shoes. (7) That's why building the park across the road doesn't make sense.

(8) Bake sales are a very good way to make money for projects. (9) Mayor LeRoux does not want to have an in-line skating park behind the school parking lot. (10) She believes the traffic from the parking lot might be dangerous to the skaters. (11) Since we have a location and money, we can start planning.

1. **What is wrong with Shira's opening sentence?**

   Ⓐ It is punctuated incorrectly.   Ⓒ It is an opinion.

   Ⓑ It is incomplete.   Ⓓ Nothing is wrong.

2. **Rewrite sentence 4 below so that it is a complete sentence.**

   _____

   _____

3. Which sentence should Shira remove from paragraph 2?

Ⓐ sentence 8

Ⓒ sentence 10

Ⓑ sentence 9

Ⓓ leave unchanged

4. What is the argument against the skating park in this draft?

_____

_____

_____

5. Combine sentences 5 and 6 into one sentence to make its meaning clearer.

_____

_____

6. Name one important subtopic that does not support the main idea.

_____

_____

Writer's Tip

Try writing a brief outline before you begin to write. Keep it simple. Write the main idea for each paragraph and then two or three supporting points to follow that idea.

Noodle Around

Subtopics need to further strengthen the main topics, or arguments, presented in the draft. Which question asks about subtopics? Discuss it with a friend.

Lesson 3: Composing and Revising

➤ **Now check your answers. If you answered a question incorrectly, study the correct answer.**

1. **What is wrong with Shira's opening sentence?**

   Answer Ⓒ is correct. It is an opinion not immediately supported by facts.

2. **Rewrite sentence 4 below so that it is a complete sentence.**

   This sentence needs a closing phrase. One way to revise the sentence is to write:

   I believe that our school needs a place for kids to in-line skate.

3. **Which sentence should Shira remove from paragraph 2?**

   Answer Ⓐ is correct. It does not link to the main idea in the paragraph.

4. **What is the argument against the skating park in this draft?**

   Mayor LeRoux believes it would be dangerous to build a skating park near a parking lot. The traffic is dangerous to skaters.

5. **Combine sentences 5 and 6 into one sentence to make its meaning clearer.**

   Answers will vary. Be sure your new sentence doesn't repeat information.
   Building the skating park near the fieldhouse would make it easy for kids to change into their skates and store their shoes.

6. **Name one important subtopic that does not support the main idea.**

   Shira does not explain how the bake sale can help her school build its skating park.

➤ **Here is a chance to work on your composing and revising skills. Answer the questions on the next three pages.**

1. Letters have specific parts, including an opening, a body, and a closing. Here is a form letter to the editor of a newspaper. Fill out this form, writing a letter that argues against the closing of your favorite park.

To the Editor:

_____

_____

_____

_____

_____

_____

_____

                                        Sincerely,

                              _____

2. Number the following sentences in chronological order, starting with the future action and ending with the past action.

   a. _____ They began construction.

   b. _____ They will begin construction.

   c. _____ They are beginning construction.

   d. _____ They had begun construction.

3. Repeated information distracts readers. Rewrite the following sentences into one sentence.

We don't understand why the school board refuses to vote on the park proposal. The school board has had many chances to decide on the in-line skating park proposal. Last month the proposal came to a vote.

_____

_____

4. Words like *sale* and *sail* sound the same but have different meanings. Such words are called homonyms. Circle the correct word to complete each sentence.

   a. I need to (bail / bale) the water out of the boat.

   b. There is a (fowl / foul) smell coming from that garbage can.

   c. My voice was (horse / hoarse) from all the cheering.

5. When you're trying to persuade someone to support your argument, it's important to be clear about your ideas. Rewrite the following sentences so that they are clear and correct.

   a. Last week Mrs. Osburn and Mrs. Weedman she started the raffle for the saving the park.

_____

_____

   b. A hundred tickets they sold well in one day I think or maybe two hundred.

_____

_____

6. Sometimes the best way to make an argument is to acknowledge that your opponent has a point. Imagine that a favorite park of yours is being closed because the city mayor wants to open up a new day care center for the working parents in your neighborhood. Write a sentence that shows you understand why the mayor wants to do this.

    _____

    _____

7. Now write down three strong pros for saving your park, using complete sentences. Circle the pro you think will best convince the city mayor that the park is worth saving.

    _____

    _____

    _____

8. Take your strongest pro from question 7 and use it to write a brief closing paragraph for a *letter to the editor*.

    _____

    _____

    _____

    _____

Lesson 3: Composing and Revising

➤ **Read the rest of Shira's draft of her persuasive essay. This section has groups of underlined words. Editing questions will be asked about them.**

> (12) Many people think that in-line skating is risky and <u>dangerus</u>. (13) As in many sports, skaters <u>can has</u> serious accidents. (14) But if you wear kneepads, shinguards, wristguards, and a helmet, you can protect yourself. (15) You can be safe in a skating park. (16) The surface can be made of <u>shock absorbing material</u> that will cushion a bad fall and protect skaters' knees.
>
> (17) <u>One of the things mayor LeRoux need to know these safeguards make difference</u>. (18) Maybe then she will agree that a skating park <u>will have made</u> a good addition to our school. (19) Students <u>will explane</u> all of these things at the school assembly. (20) We need <u>you're</u> support at this meeting. (21) Please come. (22) Show our teachers how much we want this park.

1. **In sentence 13, the word *can* is known as**

   Ⓐ a verb.

   Ⓑ a noun.

   Ⓒ a helping verb.

   Ⓓ an adverb.

2. **Correct the verb agreement error in sentence 13. Rewrite the sentence.**

   _____

   _____

3. Which item is the correct version of the underlined phrase in sentence 16?

Ⓐ shockabsorbing material   Ⓒ shock, absorbing material

Ⓑ shock-absorbing material   Ⓓ correct as is

4. Rewrite sentence 17 below to correct its errors.

_____

_____

5. Sentence 18 should read

Ⓐ Maybe then she will agree that a skating park can makes a good addition to our school.

Ⓑ Maybe then she will agree that a skating park made a good addition to our school.

Ⓒ Maybe then she will agree that a skating park had made a good addition to our school.

Ⓓ Maybe then she will agree that a skating park will make a good addition to our school.

6. Sentence 20 should be rewritten as follows:

Ⓐ We need you are support at this meeting.

Ⓑ We need your support at this meeting.

Ⓒ We need all you're support at this meeting.

Ⓓ No change is needed.

7. Write the two misspelled words, one from each paragraph, correctly in the space below.

_____

_____

➤ **Now check your answers. If you answered a question incorrectly, study the correct answer.**

1. In sentence 13, the word *can* is known as

   Answer Ⓒ is correct; *can* is a helping, or auxiliary, verb.

2. Correct the verb agreement error in sentence 13.

   The sentence should be edited as follows:

   As in many sports, skaters can have serious accidents.

3. Which item is the correct version of the underlined phrase in sentence 16?

   Answer Ⓑ is correct. The modifier *shock-absorbing* needs to be hyphenated.

4. Rewrite sentence 17 to correct its errors.

   Answers may vary, but you should correct the capitalization error, the verb agreement, and the sentence structure:

   Mayor LeRoux needs to know that these safeguards make a difference.

5. Sentence 18 should read

   Answer Ⓓ is correct. Both Mayor LeRoux's action of agreement and the school's action of building the park are in the future.

6. Sentence 20 should be rewritten as follows:

   Answer Ⓑ is correct. *You're* is a contraction for *you are*. This sentence needs a possessive pronoun—*your* support.

7. Write the two misspelled words, one from each paragraph, correctly in the space below.

   Dangerus / dangerous; explane / explain

©2001 Options Publishing, Inc.

➤ **Here is a chance to work on your editing skills. Answer the questions on the next three pages.**

1. **Correct the errors in the following sentences by using the editing symbols found on page 112.**

   a. At doctor Miller's office I read my new magazine.

   b. She told her Mother she never wanted to go to the Doctor again.

   c. Have you read the wind in the willows?

   d. It's too bad mrs. Boone can't come to the play.

2. **Many people make the mistake of using possessive forms for contractions and vice versa. Sometimes they leave out apostrophes entirely. Correct all of the errors you see in the following paragraph.**

   Its plain to see that your nervous about the test. But you're not going to fail if your prepared. A test is only as scary as it's questions, after all! Were going to study together this time. I need you're help, too.

3. **One of the most common spelling errors is forgetting a vowel in words with vowel combinations, like _explane_ for _explain_. Test yourself by circling the correctly spelled word in each pair below.**

   a. receive / receve

   b. revival / revieval

   c. reacent / recent

   d. raincoat / rayncoat

Writer's Tip

Try exchanging papers with a friend and correcting each other's mistakes. Different eyes find different problems. Remember, no one is perfect, so make your corrections constructive, not cutting.

Lesson 4: Editing

4. **Verb agreement helps readers understand who is doing what. Circle the correct verb forms in the sentences.**

   a. They (trying / tried) not to have too many accidents.

   b. If you can (learned / learn) to fall easily, it (becomes / becoming) much less hazardous.

   c. Keeping your body rigid during a fall (made / makes) you more prone to bruises and breaks.

   d. We (were / are) now ready to schedule a safety class for skaters.

5. **Spelling errors detract from good writing. Circle each misspelled word in the following paragraph.**

   I think safty is the most important thing to learn when you go skating. Always whear a helmet along with shin, elbow, and knee gards. These gards will stop you from hurting yourself. If you skate slowly, then you will stay in control. But if you skate fast, and you don't know how to stop, you mite get hurt.

6. **Incorrect usage is confusing to readers. Choose the best replacement for the underlined words in the following sentence.**

   Keeping your skates <u>in very goodest</u> shape is the best way to make them last.

   Ⓐ more better   Ⓒ in very good care
   Ⓑ in the best possible shape   Ⓓ no change necessary

7. **Another tricky punctuation problem is using hyphens in adjectives that describe nouns. Single adjectives generally do not need a hyphen. Compound adjectives with two or more words generally need hyphens. Insert hyphens correctly in the following sentences using this editing mark** ⋁⁄ **.**

   a. My ten year old cousin goes to a great elementary school.

   b. They have an ice hockey rink and the seats at the rink are covered with navy blue fleece fabric.

   c. My cousin wants to play rear guard receiver, but I think she should stick to figure skating.

   d. I guess that's because I don't like to go to the early morning skating classes by myself!

8. **Review the use of apostrophes in contractions. Circle each word or phrase that uses an apostrophe incorrectly in the following paragraph.**

   You're always wise to take skating lessons if they're available in you're town. Make sure you visit the rink it's self before you begin taking classes. Good instructors can show you more besides they're tricks and gimmicks. They'll show you how to stay safe on the ice. Talk to the instructor for you're group and ask if she'll give private lessons if you'll need them.

► **Now you are going to read and evaluate a persuasive essay that Jordan wrote about a problem at his local park. His writing needs your help. Before you begin, read the checklist below.**

Writing Checklist

Jordan will earn his best score if he achieves the following:

Ideas	• Ideas are original • Topic is clearly identified • Ideas support the topic
Organization	• Ideas are related and presented in correct order • Strong beginning, middle, and end
Creativity and Word Choice	• Words used appropriately • Creative descriptions • Words enhance ideas
Sentence Structure	• Complete sentences • Clearly written and easy to understand
Spelling and Punctuation	• Few or no errors

Directions: Write a persuasive essay about an issue affecting a park in your town or city. Present your argument and support it with facts and details.

Bike Trails for All Types

(1) My sister hates having to ride her bike near joggers. (2) Last year the bike path at our local park was the one called "The Terminator" was closed and all the bikers had to share the paths. (3) We cant have this happen again. (4) Our parks must have different trails for bikers and walkers. (5) Without seprate trails people could have gotten hurt. (6) Another good examle is my friend Anya. (7) Who is a cyclist and the winner of our county cycle-a-thon.

(8) Parks with bike paths and walking paths give each group a place to do their activity without disturbing others. (9) Bike paths need to have enough room for bikers to pass each other. (10) Walking paths don't need to be as wide, and they can also have more places to stop like benches. (11) On other words, the two kinds of paths are completely different.

(12) We are all very tired of trying to share the one path at Trenchard common Park. (13) Bicyclists find it difficult to manuever around walkers, and people who are walking or running don't want to keep watching out for bicyclists. (14) Our public parks need more of both kinds of paths for both kids of athletes.

(15) Our parks are supposed to be for everyone. (16) Not just people who like to walk or jog. (17) Lots of people ride bicycles, not just kids. (18) People of all ages and stages in life partisipate in cycling. (19) You might see children on tricycles, older kids on bikes, or parents with infant seets. (20) It's not like only a few people want bike paths. (21) Many people in our community would use them.

(22) These paths would also benefit many people in our community. (23) They includes cyclists, runners, and even picnickers. (24) We had our class picnic at Trenchard Common Park. (25) If we have areas for different activities than on one place gets too crowded. (26) Everyone will have a place to do our favorite things.

➤ **Now answer the questions about Jordan's essay.**

1. Persuasive essays need an introduction that explains the argument or opinion you are about to present. Write an introduction for Jordan's essay.

_____

_____

_____

_____

_____

2. Rewrite sentence 2 on the lines below so that it is clear and correct.

_____

_____

3. Sentence 7 is an example of a

ⓐ run-on sentence.   ⓒ redundant sentence.

ⓑ sentence fragment.   ⓓ sentence that is OK as is.

4. Find at least four misspelled words in the story. Write them below and give their correct spellings.

_____   _____

_____   _____

5. **Can you think of another example for Jordan of why city parks should have separate paths for bikers, walkers, or joggers?**

_____

_____

_____

6. **Sentences 11 and 25 are examples of poor word choice in Jordan's essay. Rewrite the sentences to help Jordan improve his score.**

_____

_____

7. **Sentence 12 has a capitalization error. Rewrite the sentence below.**

_____

_____

8. **Which is the topic sentence for the third paragraph?**

Ⓐ sentence 12   Ⓒ sentence 14

Ⓑ sentence 13   Ⓓ There is no topic sentence.

9. Find three examples of incorrect punctuation. Rewrite the sentences using the correct punctuation.

_____

_____

_____

_____

10. How should sentences 15 and 16 be changed? Write a new sentence below.

_____

_____

11. A strong conclusion should restate the writer's argument or opinion. Revise Jordan's conclusion to restate his argument and improve his essay's score.

_____

_____

_____

_____

12. Did Jordan's essay persuade you of the need for separate paths? Explain your answer.

_____

_____

Lesson 5: Evaluate Writing

Evaluate Jordan's Writing

> **Here is a guide for evaluating writing. It is called a rubric. Use this rubric to evaluate Jordan's essay.**

Writing Rubric

Score	Ideas	Organization	Creativity and Word Choice	Sentence Structure	Spelling and Punctuation
4	• Ideas are original • Topic is clearly identified • Ideas support the topic	• Ideas are related and presented in correct order • Strong beginning, middle, and end	• Words used appropriately • Creative descriptions • Words enhance ideas	• Complete sentences • Clearly written and easy to understand	• Few or no errors
3	• Some ideas are original • Most ideas support the topic	• Most ideas are related and presented in correct order • Good beginning, middle, and end	• Most words used appropriately • Some creative descriptions • Words support ideas	• Many sentences are complete • Most sentences are clearly written and easy to understand	• Some errors
2	• Few ideas are original • Ideas wander from topic • Some details support the topic	• Some ideas are related and presented in correct order • Weak beginning, middle, and end	• Some words used appropriately • Few creative descriptions	• Some run-on or fragmented sentences • Some sentences are unclear	• Many errors
1	• Ideas are incomplete • Few details support the topic	• Few ideas are related and presented in correct order • No real beginning, middle, and end	• Few words used appropriately • No attempt at creative descriptions	• Several run-on or fragmented sentences • Many sentences are unclear	• Serious errors
0	• No attempt	• No attempt	• No attempt	• No attempt	• No attempt

► **Give Jordan a score of 0 to 4 for each category. Explain why you gave him that score.**

score

Ideas _____

_____

_____

score

Organization _____

_____

_____

score

Creativity and Word Choice _____

_____

_____

score

Sentence Structure _____

_____

_____

score

Spelling and Punctuation _____

_____

Lesson 5: Evaluate Writing

➤ **Read the directions below. Then, read the checklist that you and your teacher will use to evaluate your writing.**

Directions: Imagine your favorite natural place in the world. Now imagine that someone has bought that place and plans to turn it into a shopping mall. Write an essay arguing that your favorite place should not be changed. You may include in your argument your experiences and memories, but be sure to convince your reader with solid reasoning.

Writing Checklist

I will earn my best score if I achieve the following:

Ideas	• Ideas are original • Topic is clearly identified • Ideas support the topic
Organization	• Ideas are related and presented in correct order • Strong beginning, middle, and end
Creativity and Word Choice	• Words used appropriately • Creative descriptions • Words enhance ideas
Sentence Structure	• Complete sentences • Clearly written and easy to understand
Spelling and Punctuation	• Few or no errors

Plan Your Writing

➤ **Use these pages to plan your writing. You might find this graphic organizer helpful.**

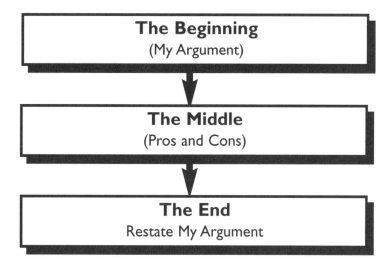

```
┌─────────────────────────────┐
│       The Beginning         │
│       (My Argument)         │
└─────────────────────────────┘
              │
              ▼
┌─────────────────────────────┐
│        The Middle           │
│      (Pros and Cons)        │
└─────────────────────────────┘
              │
              ▼
┌─────────────────────────────┐
│          The End            │
│     Restate My Argument     │
└─────────────────────────────┘
```

_____

_____

_____

_____

_____

Writer's Tip

Exchange your plans and ideas with a friend. Ask your friend to tell you if he or she sees a way for you to improve your ideas.

_____

_____

Lesson 6: Your Turn to Write

Plan Your Writing

Writer's Tip

As you write, decide if each detail supports a fact. If it doesn't, delete it and find another detail that does.

_____

_____

_____

_____

_____

_____

_____

_____

_____

_____

_____

_____

_____

_____

_____

_____

_____

_____

_____

_____

Writer's Tip

Know the difference between stating an opinion and presenting a fact. If you can test a statement, it is a fact. If you can't test it, it is probably an opinion.

_____

_____

_____

_____

Writer's Tip

Exchange your writing with a partner. You will be able to find places for improvement in each other's work more easily than you can find them in your own essay.

_____

_____

_____

_____

Lesson 6: Your Turn to Write

Write Your Final Draft

➤ **Use all the skills you have learned in this unit to score well on a final draft. Remember to carefully proofread your work before you give it to your teacher.**

1 _____

2 _____

3 _____

4 _____

5 _____

6 _____

7 _____

8 _____

9 _____

10 _____

11 _____

12 _____

13 _____

14 _____

15 _____

16 _____

17 _____

18 _____

19 _____

20 _____

21 _____

22 _____

23 _____

24 _____

25 _____

26 _____

27 _____

28 _____

29 _____

30 _____

31 _____

32 _____

33 _____

Evaluate Your Writing

➤ **Here is the same rubric you used to evaluate Jordan's essay. Now use it to evaluate your own persuasive essay.**

Writing Rubric

Score	Ideas	Organization	Creativity and Word Choice	Sentence Structure	Spelling and Punctuation
4	• Ideas are original • Topic is clearly identified • Ideas support the topic	• Ideas are related and presented in correct order • Strong beginning, middle, and end	• Words used appropriately • Creative descriptions • Words enhance ideas	• Complete sentences • Clearly written and easy to understand	• Few or no errors
3	• Some ideas are original • Most ideas support the topic	• Most ideas are related and presented in correct order • Good beginning, middle, and end	• Most words used appropriately • Some creative descriptions • Words support ideas	• Many sentences are complete • Most sentences are clearly written and easy to understand	• Some errors
2	• Few ideas are original • Ideas wander from topic • Some details support the topic	• Some ideas are related and presented in correct order • Weak beginning, middle, and end	• Some words used appropriately • Few creative descriptions	• Some run-on or fragmented sentences • Some sentences are unclear	• Many errors
1	• Ideas are incomplete • Few details support the topic	• Few ideas are related and presented in correct order • No real beginning, middle, and end	• Few words used appropriately • No attempt at creative descriptions	• Several run-on or fragmented sentences • Many sentences are unclear	• Serious errors
0	• No attempt	• No attempt	• No attempt	• No attempt	• No attempt

©2001 Options Publishing, Inc.

➤ **Give your own writing a score of 0 to 4 for each category. Explain why you gave yourself that score.**

☐
score   Ideas _____

_____

_____

☐
score   Organization _____

_____

_____

☐
score   Creativity and Word Choice _____

_____

_____

☐
score   Sentence Structure _____

_____

_____

☐
score   Spelling and Punctuation _____

_____

©2001 Options Publishing, Inc.

➤ **Have you ever imagined being somewhere else? Imagine that you are sitting in a classroom—but in a completely different time and place. Where are you, and what are you doing? Write your response on the lines below.**

_____

_____

ANCIENT EDUCATION

A relief of a Roman school

Did you know that schools have been around for thousands of years? The ancient Romans had schools, but only for a few select students. What we know about schools in ancient Rome comes mostly from historic writing. For instance, the famous poet Horace wrote quite a bit about the good and bad experiences he had in school. This gave historians a glimpse into ancient Roman education.

Education in ancient Rome was very practical. Roman children spent much of their time at home with their parents. Parents taught children the skills they needed for their future lives in the home and on the farm. Children learned family traditions, proper speech and behavior, reading and writing, and simple arithmetic. Girls learned important skills like spinning, weaving, sewing, and running a household. Boys followed along with their fathers as they worked.

Abacus

There were three levels of school in ancient Rome: elementary, grammar, and rhetoric. At about age seven, many boys and some girls went to elementary school. They studied reading and pronunciation, and they practiced writing on wax tablets. Students did not have many books to read, so they did a lot of memorization of facts. Students did most of their arithmetic in their heads. They also used their fingers and the abacus, a set of sliding beads in rows. The abacus could help with addition, subtraction, multiplication, and division.

Most children did not attend school past elementary school. Only boys who would be senators or other public figures needed to study further. A small number of boys went on to grammar school. There they studied Greek and Latin poetry in more detail. Grammar schools also taught geography, mythology, history, ethics, music, and geometry. The boys studied elocution, the art of speaking properly.

Only a few boys went to rhetoric school. This level of school was similar to modern college. There they studied public speaking skills. They also studied composition and prose literature. Young men in these upper-level schools were usually from wealthy families. Rhetoric school prepared them for public life.

The top of a Roman school table inlaid with marble

➤ **Maria's class has been asked to write a report that compares and contrasts modern American education and ancient Roman education. To begin, Maria created a Venn diagram to organize her thoughts. Use this diagram to answer questions 1–3.**

Modern American Schools

- Boys and girls study outside the home
- Boys and girls do further study

Boys and girls start school together

Ancient Roman Schools

- Rome is a cool city
- Only boys do further study

1. **Which of the following items should be added to Maria's Venn diagram?**

   Ⓐ Roman boys and girls studied at home with parents

   Ⓑ American schools are great

   Ⓒ I go to Charleston Elementary

   Ⓓ Roman schools were old

2. **Which item does not belong in Maria's Venn diagram? Explain your answer.**

   _____

   _____

3. **Write two more questions Maria could research to find out how education in ancient Rome compares with that in America today.**

   _____

   _____

➤ **Maria has found a book about Roman culture for her report on education. Use the table of contents to answer questions 4–6.**

Table of Contents

Chapter One: *Cities and Towns*

Chapter Two: *Home Life*

Chapter Three: *Public Life*

Chapter Four: *Children*

Chapter Five: *The Army*

Chapter Six: *Roman Authors*

4. **Which chapter is likely to contain the most information about education?**

   Ⓐ Three   Ⓒ Four

   Ⓑ Six   Ⓓ One

5. **Which chapter might explain what girls learned from their mothers?**

   Ⓐ One   Ⓒ Six

   Ⓑ Five   Ⓓ Two

6. **Maria wants to know more information. She will use a computer to search the Internet. What keywords will get her the MOST information on ancient Roman culture, without getting modern information?**

   Ⓐ *Rome*   Ⓒ *Ancient Rome*

   Ⓑ *Romans*   Ⓓ *Roman Education*

©2001 Options Publishing, Inc.

Writer's Tip

Who is the expert? Sometimes, you are! When you get an assignment, think about what you already know. Even if you only know a little about something, you can use what you know to help you find more information.

Noodle Around

Writers use specific words called *keywords* to focus an Internet search. Which question helps Maria focus her search? Discuss it with a friend.

Lesson 2: Prewriting and Referencing

➤ **Now check your answers. If you answered a question incorrectly, study the correct answer.**

1. **Which of the following items should be added to Maria's Venn diagram?**

   Answer Ⓐ is correct. Maria has not listed where Roman children went to school.

2. **Which item does not belong in Maria's Venn diagram? Explain your answer.**

   The fact that Rome is a cool city is not relevant to Maria's topic about ancient Roman and modern American education today.

3. **Write two more questions Maria could research to find out how education in ancient Rome compares with that in America today.**

   Answers might include:

   How long was the school day in ancient Rome? What did the school buildings look like in Rome? Do all American children go to the same kind of school? What kinds of careers do American schools prepare students for?

4. **Which chapter is likely to contain the most information about education?**

   Answer Ⓒ is correct. Chapter Four on children is likely to have the most.

5. **Which chapter might explain what girls learned from their mothers?**

   Answer Ⓓ is correct. Chapter Two is about home life. Girls learned at home from their mothers the skills they would need when they grew up.

6. **What keywords will get her the MOST information on ancient Roman culture, without getting modern information?**

   Answer Ⓒ is correct. *Roman Education* might also be useful after Maria has explored the *Ancient Rome* resources.

Try It

► **Here is a chance to work on your prewriting and referencing skills. Answer the questions on the next three pages.**

1. **Asking yourself questions is a great way to find out about what you do or do not know about a subject. Answer these six questions about the topic** *School in Your Town.*

Who? _____

What? _____

When? _____

Where? _____

Why? _____

How? _____

2. **You can compare things in different ways. One way is to write all the characteristics of one thing, and then write all the characteristics of the other thing. Another method is to compare characteristics as you go along.**

   a. First, describe some of the characteristics of your school.

   _____

   _____

   b. Second, describe some of the characteristics of the high school you will attend. If you are not sure, describe a friend's or relative's school.

   _____

   _____

Lesson 2: Prewriting and Referencing

3. Now try the second comparison method. Choose three characteristics that both schools have—for example, lunchrooms, classrooms, and gymnasiums. Write your three below.

_____   _____   _____

4. Write at least three sentences comparing and contrasting those three characteristics.

_____

_____

_____

_____

5. Imagine that you are introducing a student from another country to your school. What would you want to tell this student? Would you like to give the student directions around the school? Maybe you would choose to explain school customs and behaviors. Using the technique of brainstorming, spend five minutes writing down your ideas.

_____

_____

_____

_____

_____

6. Your teacher has told you that a new student comes from India. Find out something about this country and its school life. Use a computer in your school or library to search the Internet and find at least three sources that will give you information about schools in India. Record your information here.

_____

_____

_____

_____

_____

_____

7. Complete the following Venn diagram to compare schools in India to the United States.

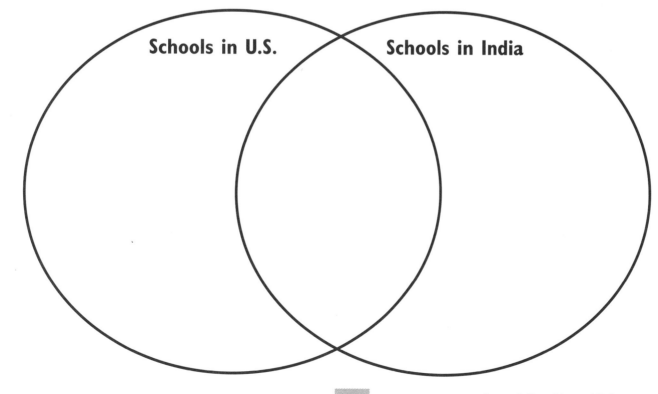

Schools in U.S.   Schools in India

©2001 Options Publishing, Inc.

▶ **Maria has completed her research. Read this part of Maria's rough draft. Then answer questions 1–6.**

(1) American children usually begin their education when they are four or five. (2) Some children ride the bus to elementary school. (3) They remain in school through their teenage years. (4) After that, some of them go to college. (5) Young adults study many subjects to prepare them for their careers and adulthood. (6) They study reading writing and arithmetic in elementary school. (7) Both boys and girls attend school.

(8) Children in ancient Rome didn't attend school for as many years as modern American children. (9) Boys and girls stayed at home, taught to read and write and do other things by their parents. (10) Later some boys went to a more advanced school. (11) Girls stayed at home and continued to learn what women needed to know, like cooking and polite manners, from her mother. (12) Boys went with their fathers to prepare for their careers. (13) Boys also went to advanced school to study for their careers.

1. **Reorder the sentences in the first paragraph so that they read logically. Write the numbers of the sentences in the new order below.**

   _____

   _____

2. **Which sentence could you delete from paragraph 1 without changing the general meaning of the paragraph?**

   Ⓐ sentence 6   Ⓒ sentence 2

   Ⓑ sentence 1   Ⓓ sentence 5

3. **What could Maria add to sentence 5 to make it more relevant to the essay?**

   (A) a list of school subjects

   (B) a list of schools' names

   (C) a list of students' names

   (D) no change needed

4. **What is wrong with sentence 9? Identify the problem and rewrite the sentence.**

   _____

   _____

   _____

Writer's Tip

As you write your first draft, remember to stick to your outline. Go back and refer to it often; that's the easiest way to make sure you don't get off track.

5. **The mistake in sentence 11 is a problem with**

   (A) incomplete information or a sentence fragment.

   (B) verb tense.

   (C) noun-pronoun agreement.

   (D) verb agreement.

6. **Suggest two things Maria could add to paragraph 2 to make it more informative.**

   _____

   _____

Noodle Around

Informative essays provide in-depth information about a topic. Which question helps Maria better inform her readers? Discuss your answer with a friend.

Lesson 3: Composing and Revising

➤ **Now check your answers. If you answered a question incorrectly, study the correct answer.**

1. **Reorder the sentences in the first paragraph so that they read logically.**

   The most logical order is 1, 7, 2, 6, 3, 5, and 4.

2. **Which sentence could you delete from paragraph 1 without changing the general meaning of the paragraph?**

   The answer is Ⓒ, sentence 2. It is not necessary to know how the children get to school to make sense of this paragraph.

3. **What could Maria add to sentence 5 to make it more relevant to the essay?**

   Answer Ⓐ is correct. A list of school subjects would add relevant information to the sentence.

4. **What is wrong with sentence 9? Identify the problem and rewrite the sentence to help Maria score higher.**

   This sentence is a run-on. A revision might be:
   Boys and girls were taught to read and write at home by their mothers.

5. **The mistake in sentence 11 is a problem with**

   Answer Ⓒ is correct. The sentence should show agreement between *girls* and *their*.

6. **Suggest two things Maria could add to paragraph 2 to make it more informative.**

   Answers will vary, but students might suggest subjects boys learned with their mothers or the ages of children when they went to school.

Try It

> **Here is a chance to work on your composing and revising skills. Answer the questions on the next three pages.**

1. **Which of the following could be added to an informative essay about school in ancient Rome?**

   Ⓐ a description of the Romans' clothing

   Ⓑ the story of Horace

   Ⓒ some of the things students wrote on their wax tablets

   Ⓓ Roman children's toys

2. **One way to add clarity and variety to your writing is to begin sentences with a prepositional phrase. Prepositional phrases tell more about the action. Rewrite each sentence below so it begins with a prepositional phrase.**

   a. The class waited patiently while their teacher graded the final exams.

   _____

   b. All of the students were anxious to know if they had passed the tests before vacation started.

   _____

   c. Summer school will be held between the Fourth of July and Labor Day.

   _____

   d. No one wants to be left behind in the classroom with all of the beach activities scheduled.

   _____

3. When you are revising your first draft, check that your details link to your topic. Underline the information in the paragraph below that strays from the topic.

Researching historic topics can be a challenge, but it can also be very interesting. Because history covers so many areas, finding information on one specific topic or time period may frustrate you. Someone once said, "Those who forget history are doomed to repeat it." There are some steps you can take to make your research less frustrating, just like gathering your materials before you make a cake means easier baking. First, make sure you've read your assignment carefully and haven't just skimmed over it like all those other times. Does your teacher want you to write about a large topic, or does the assignment have a narrower focus? Once my teacher assigned us an essay about the kings of England.

4. Incomplete sentences leave the reader hanging by introducing unfinished ideas. Rewrite each sentence fragment into a complete sentence.

a. Children in ancient Rome.

_____

b. Parents at home.

_____

5. Complete the following statement: The main objective of informative writing is to

Ⓐ entertain the reader.   Ⓒ persuade the reader.

Ⓑ convince the reader.   Ⓓ inform the reader.

6. **Which set of sentences presents redundant information? Fill in the circle for the sentences that are redundant.**

   Ⓐ American children go to school at age four or five. Children in America start school at four or five years of age.

   Ⓑ Girls learned from their mothers. Roman mothers taught their daughters how to read and write.

   Ⓒ Boys went to advanced school to learn advanced subjects. Boys went on to study logic in advanced schools.

7. **Short sentences can break the reader's flow. Combine the following sentences into a complex sentence without changing the meaning.**

   The coliseum was a large building. It housed sporting and entertainment events.

   _____

   _____

8. **What is Maria's objective, or reason, for writing an informative essay about ancient Roman schools and modern schools? Write her objective below.**

   _____

   _____

9. **Did Maria stick to her objective from page 78 when writing the first part of her informative essay ? Explain your answer.**

   _____

   _____

   _____

➤ **Now read the rest of Maria's rough draft. This section has groups of underlined words. Editing questions will be asked about them.**

---

(14) American children <u>don't hardly ever</u> stay home for schooling. (15) When <u>they goes</u> to kindergarten, they start twelve years of school. (16) First there is elementary school, then middle school, then junior high and finally high school. (17) Every day they stay in school for about seven hours. (18) <u>Their teachers are in charge of them. During this time.</u>

(19) <u>Roman children werent exspected to remain children for very long.</u> (20) Boys and girls stayed with their parents so they could learn about the <u>dutys</u> adults had. (21) Very young children had toys, but older children simply learned beside the grown ups. (22) American <u>kids</u> don't know as much about what their parents do.

---

1. **The error in sentence 14 should be corrected as follows:**

   Ⓐ hardly never.   Ⓒ hardly ever.

   Ⓑ don't ever.   Ⓓ No correction is needed.

2. **Rewrite sentence 18 so that it begins with a prepositional phrase.**

   _____

   _____

3. **Which sentence contains an error in verb agreement?**

   Ⓐ sentence 15   Ⓒ sentence 21

   Ⓑ sentence 20   Ⓓ sentence 14

4. Sentence 19 contains spelling and punctuation errors. Write sentence 19 correctly below.

_____

_____

5. What informal word does Maria use in the second paragraph? Write the word and a more formal replacement for it below.

_____

6. One misspelled word in paragraph 2 is an incorrect plural. Write it and the correct form below.

_____

_____

Writer's Tip

One of the best editing tools is reading aloud. You don't need an audience—just read to yourself. Hearing what you've written gives you a different way of recognizing mistakes.

Noodle Around

Informal words, or slang, can detract from informative writing. Which question helps Maria replace her informal words for formal ones? Discuss it with a friend.

Lesson 4: Editing

➤ **Now check your answers. If you answered a question incorrectly, study the correct answer.**

1. **The error in sentence 14 should be corrected as follows:**

   Answer Ⓒ is correct. Two negative constructions next to each other are known as a *double negative.*

2. **Rewrite sentence 18 so that it begins with a preposition.**

   The sentence should be edited as follows:

   During this time, their teachers are in charge of them.

3. **Which sentence contains an error in verb agreement?**

   Answer Ⓐ is correct: *they goes* should be *they go.*

4. **Sentence 19 contains spelling and punctuation errors. Write sentence 19 correctly below.**

   Roman children weren't expected to remain children for very long.

5. **What informal word does Maria use in the second paragraph? Write the word and a more formal replacement for it below.**

   The informal word is *kids*; the replacement is *children.*

6. **One misspelled word in paragraph 2 is an incorrect plural. Write it and the correct form below.**

   The plural of *duty* is *duties.*

➤ **Here is a chance to work on your editing skills. Answer the questions on the next three pages.**

1. **Checking the correct spelling of plurals is an important step in editing. Use a dictionary and form the plurals of the following words.**

   a. schoolhouse _____

   b. hobby _____

   c. bookshelf _____

   d. essay _____

2. **Using informal language in informative writing can make it appear less believable. Rewrite the following sentences so that they don't contain any slang.**

   After school we hang out at my best bud's place. His comic book collection is so cool that we can chill for ages.

   _____

   _____

3. **Using quotation marks correctly is an important skill. Commas are also an important part of writing a direct quote correctly. Practice adding quotation marks and commas correctly by editing the following sentences. Use these editing marks ⌄ ⌄ ⋀ to show where the punctuation marks go.**

   a. Allie said I owe everything to my teacher who taught me so much.

   b. Mrs. Makeba said When I retire I'd like to know at least one student's life has changed for the better because of me.

Lesson 4: Editing

4. **Edit the following pairs of sentences by making them into a complex sentence. Remember to remove any unnecessary words by using this symbol ℒ . Add words using this symbol ∧ .**

a. My great-grandmother taught third grade in the 1920s. My great-grandmother taught 40 students of all ages in a one-room school.

b. The students did some activities together, but they all had different reading levels. They did their reading work in separate groups.

c. Every night my great-grandmother had to correct each student's work. Each student had work that needed to be graded before the next lesson.

5. **A common grammatical mistake is known as a double negative. Rewrite the following sentences to remove the double negatives.**

a. I can't never get my paper route finished in the morning.

_____

b. My mother hardly doesn't try anymore to help me deliver the papers.

_____

c. Pretty soon Mr. Rice won't have me do no more work.

_____

d. If I don't work none, I won't have hardly any money for a new bike.

_____

e. Without a new bike, I can't do none of my job.

_____

6. **Verb agreement means that the subject of the sentence and the verb in the sentence agree in number. Edit each sentence so that the subject and the verb agree.**

   a. Donna and I was going to the library and then swimming.

   _____

   _____

   b. My parents and I was going out to eat last night.

   _____

   _____

   c. Tonight we goes to the movies with Cory.

   _____

   _____

7. **Now take those three sentences and edit them so that all the subjects are singular.**

   _____

   _____

   _____

   _____

Lesson 4: Editing

► **In this lesson you will read a process, or how-to, essay that Chris wrote. His writing needs your help. Before you begin, read the checklist below.**

Writing Checklist

Chris will earn his best score if he achieves the following:

Ideas	• Ideas are original • Topic is clearly identified • Ideas support the topic
Organization	• Ideas are related and presented in correct order • Strong beginning, middle, and end
Creativity and Word Choice	• Words used appropriately • Creative descriptions • Words enhance ideas
Sentence Structure	• Complete sentences • Clearly written and easy to understand
Spelling and Punctuation	• Few or no errors

➤ **These are the directions that Chris was given.**

Directions: Studying for tests is part of everyday student life in modern America. Write a set of instructions on how to study for a test in history. Remember to include at least three steps.

(1) Studying for your history test can be as easy as one, two, three. (2) I have a proven method that will help you organize yourself and your materials. (3) To begin, you will need a timer, a notebook, and a pencil. (4) Gathering the things you needs is the first step of many on your way to terrific test grades. (5) For example, a cook has to gather ingredients and equipment before trying a recipe. (6) Some recipes have many exciting ingredients like chicken curry.

(7) First, find a comfortable chair to sit in and a desk where you can work. (8) Some people might choose to begin by reading through their class notes. (9) Or you could review the chapters you need to cover for your test. (10) If you have more than one chapter to study, you can break the reading. (11) This system works well for individual chapters as well. (12) Divide each chapter into manageable sections. (13) Heres where the clock will help you. (14) Deside how many minutes you can read without taking a break. (15) I like to read for ten minutes at a time.

Lesson 5: Evaluate Writing

(16) Set the timer for that amount of time and when the timer goes off take a brake. (17) Second, put a bookmark on the page you've reached and close your book. (18) Now your going to work from memory. (19) Set the time again, this time for a shorter time. (20) In your notebook, write down as many important facts as you can remember. (21) _____

(22) _____

(23) The third step combines your work from the first two. (24) Compare the chapter you've reviewed with the notes you've taken. (25) Ask yourself questions like these, what did I forget, which dates or names need more information, what are the most important ideas to learn? (26) Write down your questions and answers in your notebook. (27) Use all of your notes to revew for the test.

(28) If you follow these three steps, youll do good on your test.

➤ **Now answer the following questions about Chris's essay.**

1. How-to essays often begin with an attention-grabber; that is, a sentence that grabs the reader's attention and makes the essay seem interesting. Write an attention-grabbing opening for Chris's essay.

_____

_____

_____

2. Sentence 4 contains an error in verb agreement. Rewrite the sentence correctly below.

_____

_____

3. What is the name for the type of sentence mistake in sentence 10?

   Ⓐ incomplete sentence   Ⓒ comma splice

   Ⓑ redundant sentence   Ⓓ run-on sentence

4. Find three contraction errors in Chris's essay. Write them below.

_____

_____

_____

5. **Combine sentences 12, 13, and 14 into one complex sentence.**

_____

_____

6. **List at least four spelling errors in Chris's essay. Write the incorrect and correct versions below.**

_____

_____

_____

_____

7. **Which sentence or pair of sentences should be deleted from this essay? Explain your answer.**

Ⓐ sentence 5   Ⓒ sentences 13 and 14

Ⓑ sentences 5 and 6   Ⓓ sentences 26 and 27

_____

_____

8. **Which is the best edited version of sentence 16?**

Ⓐ Set your timer for the correct amount of time, and when it's finished take a brake.

Ⓑ Set your timer for the correct amount of time and, when its finished take a brake.

Ⓒ Set your timer for the correct amount of time, and when it's finished take a break.

Ⓓ Set your timer for the correct amount of time and, when it's finished, take a break.

9. **Paragraph 3 is unfinished. Write a possible ending for it on the lines below.**

_____

_____

_____

_____

10. **Chris has not written a proper conclusion for his essay. Write one for him on the lines below. Remember that a how-to essay should close by reminding readers of the essay's purpose.**

_____

_____

_____

_____

_____

Evaluate Chris's Writing

▶ **Here is a rubric, a guide for evaluating writing. Use this rubric to evaluate Chris's essay.**

Writing Rubric

Score	Ideas	Organization	Creativity and Word Choice	Sentence Structure	Spelling and Punctuation
4	• Ideas are original • Topic is clearly identified • Ideas support the topic	• Ideas are related and presented in correct order • Strong beginning, middle, and end	• Words used appropriately • Creative descriptions • Words enhance ideas	• Complete sentences • Clearly written and easy to understand	• Few or no errors
3	• Some ideas are original • Most ideas support the topic	• Most ideas are related and presented in correct order • Good beginning, middle, and end	• Most words used appropriately • Some creative descriptions • Words support ideas	• Many sentences are complete • Most sentences are clearly written and easy to understand	• Some errors
2	• Few ideas are original • Ideas wander from topic • Some details support the topic	• Some ideas are related and presented in correct order • Weak beginning, middle, and end	• Some words used appropriately • Few creative descriptions	• Some run-on or fragmented sentences • Some sentences are unclear	• Many errors
1	• Ideas are incomplete • Few details support the topic	• Few ideas are related and presented in correct order • No real beginning, middle, and end	• Few words used appropriately • No attempt at creative descriptions	• Several run-on or fragmented sentences • Many sentences are unclear	• Serious errors
0	• No attempt	• No attempt	• No attempt	• No attempt	• No attempt

©2001 Options Publishing, Inc.

➤ Give Chris's writing a score of 0 to 4 for each category. Explain why you gave him that score.

[ ]
score

Ideas _____

_____

_____

[ ]
score

Organization _____

_____

_____

[ ]
score

Creativity and Word Choice _____

_____

_____

[ ]
score

Sentence Structure _____

_____

_____

[ ]
score

Spelling and Punctuation _____

_____

Lesson 5: Evaluate Writing

➤ **Read the directions below. Then, read the checklist that you and your teacher will use to evaluate your writing.**

Directions: Styles in education change just like those in fashion and music. Choose someone who attended school in a different time period, such as a parent, aunt or uncle, grandparents, or neighbor. Interview the person you chose. Then, use what you learned in your interview to write an informative essay.

Writing Checklist

I will earn my best score if I achieve the following:

Ideas	• Ideas are original • Topic is clearly identified • Ideas support the topic
Organization	• Ideas are related and presented in correct order • Strong beginning, middle, and end
Creativity and Word Choice	• Words used appropriately • Creative descriptions • Words enhance ideas
Sentence Structure	• Complete sentences • Clearly written and easy to understand
Spelling and Punctuation	• Few or no errors

Plan Your Writing

➤ **Use these pages to plan your writing. You might find this graphic organizer helpful.**

Who will I interview?

Where will I conduct the interview?

When will I conduct the interview?

What materials do I need?

What questions will I ask?

How will I record the answers to my questions?

_____

_____

_____

_____

_____

_____

_____

_____

Lesson 6: Your Turn to Write

Plan Your Writing

_____

_____

_____

_____

_____

_____

_____

_____

_____

_____

_____

_____

_____

Writer's Tip

Keep a writer's notebook to store ideas and information about your topic. Writers use notebooks to remember questions, facts, or ideas that they might use later.

Writer's Tip

When editing your rough draft, look for one kind of error at a time. Then, give your writing to a friend. A second pair of eyes can catch things you might have missed.

Write Your Final Draft

➤ Use all the skills you have learned in this unit to score well on a final draft. Remember to carefully proofread your work before you give it to your teacher.

1 _____

2 _____

3 _____

4 _____

5 _____

6 _____

7 _____

8 _____

9 _____

10 _____

11 _____

12 _____

13 _____

14 _____

15 _____

16 _____

17 _____

18 _____

19 _____

20 _____

21 _____

22 _____

23 _____

24 _____

25 _____

26 _____

27 _____

28 _____

29 _____

30 _____

31 _____

32 _____

33 _____

Lesson 6: Your Turn to Write

Evaluate Your Writing

➤ **Here is the same rubric you used to evaluate Chris's essay. Now use it to evaluate your own essay.**

Writing Rubric

Score	Ideas	Organization	Creativity and Word Choice	Sentence Structure	Spelling and Punctuation
4	• Ideas are original • Topic is clearly identified • Ideas support the topic	• Ideas are related and presented in correct order • Strong beginning, middle, and end	• Words used appropriately • Creative descriptions • Words enhance ideas	• Complete sentences • Clearly written and easy to understand	• Few or no errors
3	• Some ideas are original • Most ideas support the topic	• Most ideas are related and presented in correct order • Good beginning, middle, and end	• Most words used appropriately • Some creative descriptions • Words support ideas	• Many sentences are complete • Most sentences are clearly written and easy to understand	• Some errors
2	• Few ideas are original • Ideas wander from topic • Some details support the topic	• Some ideas are related and presented in correct order • Weak beginning, middle, and end	• Some words used appropriately • Few creative descriptions	• Some run-on or fragmented sentences • Some sentences are unclear	• Many errors
1	• Ideas are incomplete • Few details support the topic	• Few ideas are related and presented in correct order • No real beginning, middle, and end	• Few words used appropriately • No attempt at creative descriptions	• Several run-on or fragmented sentences • Many sentences are unclear	• Serious errors
0	• No attempt	• No attempt	• No attempt	• No attempt	• No attempt

➤ **Give your own writing a score of 0 to 4 for each category. Explain why you gave yourself that score.**

☐ **Ideas** _____
score
_____

_____

☐ **Organization** _____
score
_____

_____

☐ **Creativity and Word Choice** _____
score
_____

_____

☐ **Sentence Structure** _____
score
_____

_____

☐ **Spelling and Punctuation** _____
score
_____

Lesson 6: Your Turn to Write

Helpful Tips

Editing Symbols		Examples
⊙	Insert a period	We went to the beach ⊙ I found lots of shells.
⌄,	Insert a comma	Our friend, Tawanda⌄is having a party.
∧	Insert a letter, word, phrase, or sentence	very It is∧cold outside.
ℯ	Take out a letter, word, or phrase	We want ice cream ~~today~~ for dessert.
≡	Change a lower-case letter to a capital letter	I saw mrs. file yesterday. ≡ ≡
/	Change a capital letter to a lower-case letter	We are going to the /Movies tonight.
SP	Check the spelling of the word	SP My litle brother is coming with us.

Use the correct punctuation mark at the end of every sentence	
Use a period for a statement or command:	I brought my lunch today.
Use a question mark for a question:	What is in your lunch?
Use an exclamation point for a sentence with feeling:	That is my favorite movie!
Use a comma	
between words in a list:	I have a dog, a cat, and a goldfish.
between two short sentences:	I was almost late, but I got there.
Use an apostrophe	
in contractions:	didn't (did not); I'm (I am)
in words that show ownership:	dog's tail; girls' team